Andrew Brodie Basics

LET'S DO PUNCTUATION

FOR AGES 5-6

- Structured punctuation practice
- Regular progress tests
- Matched to the National Curriculum

with over **100** reward stickers

Andrew Brodie
An imprint of Bloomsbury Publishing Plc

50 Bedford Square
London
WC1B 3DP
UK

1385 Broadway
New York
NY 10018
USA

www.bloomsbury.com

ANDREW BRODIE is a trademark of Bloomsbury Publishing Plc

First published in Great Britain 2017

A catalogue record for this book is available from the British Library.

ISBN
PB: 978-1-4729-4062-9
ePDF: 978-1-4729-4061-2

2 4 6 8 10 9 7 5 3 1

Designed and typeset by Marcus Duck Design
Printed and bound in China by Leo Paper Products

This book is produced using paper that is made from wood grown in managed,
sustainable forests. It is natural, renewable and recyclable. The logging and manufacturing
processes conform to the environmental regulations of the country of origin.

To find out more about our authors and books visit www.bloomsbury.com.
Here you will find extracts, author interviews, details of forthcoming events and the
option to sign up for our newsletters.

BLOOMSBURY

Notes for parents

What's in this book

This is the first in the series of *Andrew Brodie Basics: Let's Do Punctuation* books. Each book features a clearly structured approach to developing and improving children's knowledge and use of punctuation in their reading and writing.

The National Curriculum states that children in Year 1 should learn appropriate terminology in relation to grammar and punctuation, including the following:

- letter, capital letter
- word, singular, plural
- sentence
- punctuation, full stop, question mark, exclamation mark.

They will be learning to create sentences, leaving appropriate spaces between words, and to punctuate their sentences with a capital letter at the start and a full stop, question mark or exclamation mark at the end. They will be joining words and joining clauses using the word 'and'. They will be using a capital letter for names of people, places, the days of the week, and the personal pronoun 'I'.

How you can help

Make sure your child is ready for their punctuation practice and help them to enjoy the activities in this book. If necessary, read the activity out loud and discuss it so that your child really understands what the writing means. On every page there is a dotted circle where you can add a sticker to reward your child for working really hard.

The answer section

The answer section at the end of this book can be a useful teaching tool: ask your child to compare their responses to the ones shown. Their answers will not be identical but should include similar information. If your child has made mistakes, they can learn from these and do better next time. Remember that sometimes progress will seem very slow but at other times it can be surprisingly rapid.

Most importantly, enjoy the experience of working with your child. Together you can share the excitement of learning.

Rufus the Raccoon, who may tell your child what to focus on when working on the page.

Brodie's Brain Boosters, which feature quick extra activities designed to make your child think, using the skills and knowledge they already have. Can your child talk about their experiences using appropriate and interesting vocabulary? Can they then write well-punctuated sentences that give the information clearly?

Contents

There are 26 letters in the alphabet.

Here is the alphabet written in lower case letters:

a b c d e f g h i j k l m n o p q r s t u v w x y z

Write the alphabet in lower case letters.

_____

_____

Here is the alphabet written in capital letters:

A B C D E F G H I J K L M N O P Q R S T U V W X Y Z

Write the alphabet in capital letters.

_____

_____

Every name starts with a capital letter.

Write your full name.

_____

Brodie's
Brain Booster

Can you write the full name of every person in your family?

Capital letters at the start of names

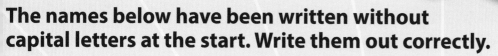

My name starts with a capital letter.

The names below have been written without capital letters at the start. Write them out correctly.

alex	_____	noah	_____
borak	_____	ola	_____
celina	_____	pierre	_____
danek	_____	qadir	_____
eli	_____	robert	_____
faye	_____	sam	_____
george	_____	tara	_____
hannah	_____	umi	_____
imogen	_____	vida	_____
jake	_____	william	_____
kim	_____	xander	_____
lara	_____	yannik	_____
mia	_____	zara	_____

Did you notice that the names have been written in alphabetical order?

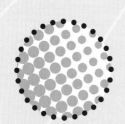

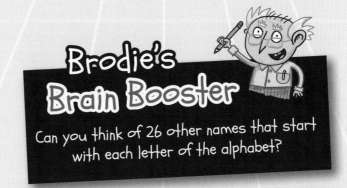

Brodie's Brain Booster

Can you think of 26 other names that start with each letter of the alphabet?

Capital letters for days

My favourite day is Saturday.

The names of the days of the week start with capital letters. The days have been written below without capital letters at the start. Write them out correctly.

sunday _____

monday _____

tuesday _____

wednesday _____

thursday _____

friday _____

saturday _____

Which two days are at the weekend?

_____   _____

What is your favourite day of the week?

_____

On which days do you go to school?

_____   _____

_____   _____

_____

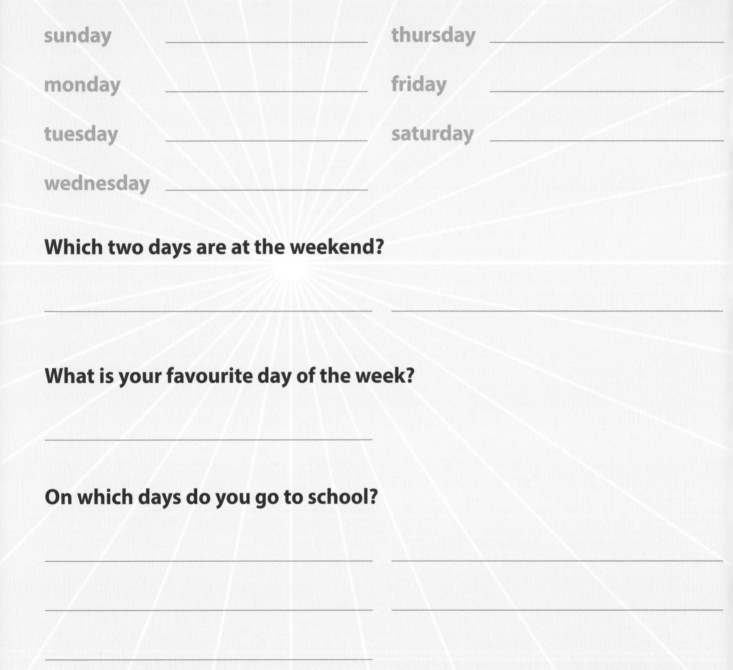

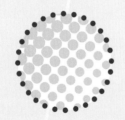

Brodie's Brain Booster

How many days are there in a fortnight?

6

Capital letters for months

My birthday is in January.

The names of the months of the year start with capital letters. The months have been written below without capital letters at the start. Write them out correctly.

january _____

february _____

march _____

april _____

may _____

june _____

july _____

august _____

september _____

october _____

november _____

december _____

Which month is it now?

_____

Which month will it be next month?

_____

In which month is your birthday?

_____

Brodie's Brain Booster

How many days are there in this month?

Capital letters for names of places

The names of places start with capital letters.

The United Kingdom includes four countries. The countries are England, Northern Ireland, Scotland and Wales.

Write the names of the countries in the correct places on the map.

....

....

....

....

Capital letters for titles

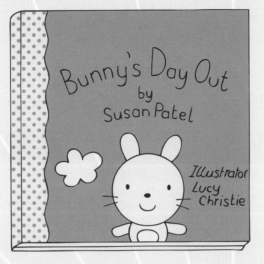

I like reading books.

This book is called *Bunny's Day Out*. The main words in the title start with capital letters.

The book was written by Susan Patel. It was illustrated by Lucy Christie. The names start with capital letters.

Look at some of your own books. Do the titles have capital letters?

Write the titles, authors and illustrators of three of your books.

_____

_____

_____

_____

_____

_____

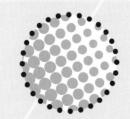

Brodie's Brain Booster

What is your favourite book?

Write the alphabet in lower case letters.
The first three letters have been done for you.

_a_ _b_ _c_ _____

_____

Write the alphabet in capital letters. The first three letters have been done for you.

_A_ _B_ _C_ _____

_____

The names below have been written without capital letters. Write them correctly.

abbi   _____   maleeha   _____

joseph   _____   imogen   _____

Write your answers to the questions below using capital letters correctly.

What day is it today? _____

What day was it yesterday? _____

What day will it be tomorrow? _____

What month is it now? _____

What is the name of the next month? _____

What is the name of the place where you live?

_____

What is the name of a place that you visit often?

_____

Sentences

My name is Mia. I am six years old.

Every sentence starts with a capital letter.

Did you notice that Mia's sentences start with capital letters?

Did you notice that the sentences end with full stops?

Now write two sentences about yourself. Don't forget the capital letters and full stops.

_____

_____

_____

_____

Brodie's Brain Booster

What age will you be next? In which month is your birthday?

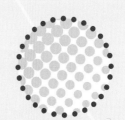

11

Sentences

Most sentences end with a full stop.

My name is Marek.
I like swimming.
I like going to football practice.

Did you notice that Marek's sentences start with capital letters?

Did you notice that the sentences end with full stops?

Write three sentences about some activities that you like. Don't forget the capital letters and full stops.

_____

_____

_____

_____

Brodie's Brain Booster

What is your favourite activity?

12

Months and seasons

Do you remember the names of all the months?

Write the months in the correct places on the seasons wheel. Some months have been written for you. Look back at page 7 if you want to.

January

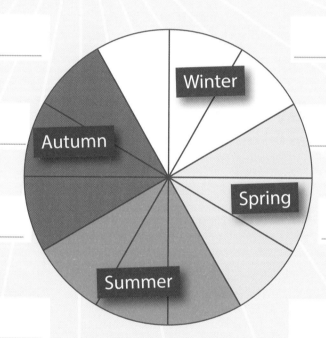

Winter

Autumn

Spring

Summer

June

Brodie's Brain Booster

Do you know the birthday month of every member of your family?

13

Family birthdays

I don't remember when my birthday is. Can you remember?

My birthday is in June.

My birthday is in October. Mum's birthday is in August.

Write about the birthday months of some members of your family. Don't forget the capital letters and full stops.

_____

_____

_____

_____

_____

Brodie's Brain Booster

What month is it now? What month is next?

Capital letter 'I'

When I am writing about myself I need a capital letter 'I'.

My name is Seth. At the weekend I go swimming. On Tuesday I have football practice.

Did you notice that Seth's sentences start with capital letters?

Did you notice that the sentences end with full stops?

Did you notice that the letter i is written as a capital when Seth is writing about himself?

Write three sentences about some things that you do. Don't forget the capital letters and full stops.

_____

_____

_____

_____

Brodie's Brain Booster

Look in your reading book. How many capital letters can you find on the first page?

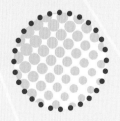

People and places

Remember that place names start with capital letters.

My nan lives in Somerset.

My grandad lives in Edinburgh.

Write some sentences about where people in your family live.

_____

_____

_____

_____

_____

Brodie's Brain Booster

How many countries can you name?

16

Write two sentences about a member
of your family.

_____

_____

_____

Write two sentences about your friend.

_____

_____

_____

Write two sentences about what you did at the weekend.

_____

_____

_____

_____

More places

We went to Cornwall on holiday. My sister and I played on the beach.

My family went to London on holiday. We went to lots of museums.

Write some sentences about your last holiday.

_____

_____

_____

_____

_____

Brodie's Brain Booster

Have you ever visited London?

Every day

Isn't Shannon's handwriting neat!

Read what Shannon has written about what she does on school days.

Every Monday I have football practice. On Tuesday
we go swimming. On Wednesday I have choir.
My nan looks after me after school on Thursdays.
We have assembly on Friday afternoon.

Write some sentences about what you do on school days.

_____

_____

_____

_____

_____

Brodie's
Brain Booster
What is your favourite thing to do
on Fridays?

Weekends

Remember that all the days of the week start with capital letters.

Read what Joe has written about what he does at the weekend.

Saturday is the best day. I play in the garden. Sometimes we go out on our bikes. On Sunday we go out for lunch.

Write some sentences about what you do at the weekend.

_____

_____

_____

_____

_____

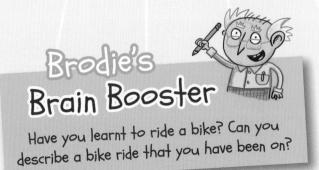

Brodie's Brain Booster

Have you learnt to ride a bike? Can you describe a bike ride that you have been on?

Rhymes

I use up quite a lot of time, trying hard to make words rhyme.

Look carefully at this rhyming poem.

On Monday morning I go to school,
On Tuesday night I dive in the pool,
Every Wednesday we go to the park,
If it gets late we play in the dark.

Did you notice that every line starts with a capital letter?

Did you notice that some lines end with a comma?

Copy the rhyme carefully.

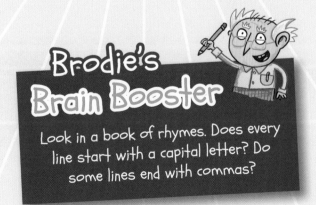

Brodie's Brain Booster

Look in a book of rhymes. Does every line start with a capital letter? Do some lines end with commas?

Another rhyme

I wonder if you have ever heard,
A poem with a rhyming word.

Look carefully at this rhyming poem.

Last Thursday I went out on my bike,
Then on Friday I went for a hike.
On Saturday I ran instead,
On Sunday I just stayed in bed.

Did you notice that every line starts with a capital letter?
Did you notice that some lines end with a comma?

Copy the rhyme carefully.

_____

_____

_____

_____

Brodie's Brain Booster

Can you practise a poem to say out loud?

22

Birthday present

Imogen was given a scooter for her birthday. It was from her grandparents. Pretend that you are Imogen. Write a thank you note.

_____

_____

_____

_____

_____

_____

Thank you!

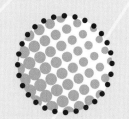

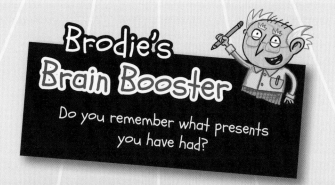

May ~~January~~ October April ~~February~~ December

July March June September August November

Finish the sentences below. Some of them have been done for you.

The first month of the year is _____*January*_____.

_____*February*_____ **is the second month.**

The third month is _____.

The next month is _____.

_____ **is the fifth month.**

The sixth month is _____.

The seventh month is _____.

_____ **is next.**

The ninth month is _____.

The tenth month is _____.

The eleventh month is _____.

The last month of the year is _____.

Questions

I can think of lots of questions.

How old are you?

I am six years old.

The girl asked the boy a question. Her question sentence ended with a question mark instead of a full stop.

Start here ——→ ?

Finish with a dot. ←——

Practise writing question marks.

?   ?   ?   ?

Now try writing smaller question marks.

?   ?   ?   ?

Brodie's Brain Booster

Look in your reading book. Can you find any questions?

I can think of lots of questions but not many answers.

What is your name?

My name is Tanya.

The boy asked the girl a question. His question sentence ended with a question mark.

Copy the questions and the answers. Remember when to use capital letters. Remember when to use full stops and when to use question marks.

What is your name?

_____

My name is Tanya.

_____

How old are you?

_____

I am six years old.

_____

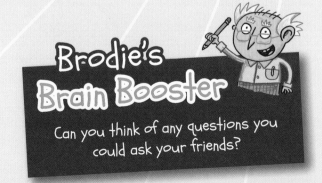

Brodie's Brain Booster

Can you think of any questions you could ask your friends?

Writing questions

Can you think of three questions to ask your friend or a member of your family? Write the questions out carefully. They can be about anything you like!

Question 1:

_____

_____

Question 2:

_____

_____

Question 3:

_____

_____

Did you remember to put capital letters in the right places?

Did you remember to put question marks at the end of the sentences?

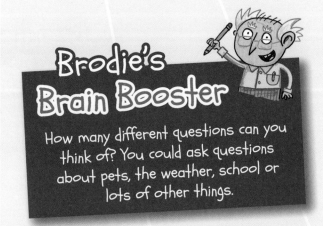

Brodie's Brain Booster

How many different questions can you think of? You could ask questions about pets, the weather, school or lots of other things.

Writing answers

I don't know many answers.

Ask your friend or a member of your family to answer your questions. Write their answers out carefully.

Answer 1:

_____

_____

Answer 2:

_____

_____

Answer 3:

_____

_____

Did you remember to put capital letters in the right places?

Did you remember to put full stops at the end of the sentences?

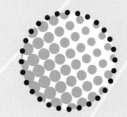

Brodie's Brain Booster

What questions do you find difficult to answer?

28

I like questions about food. I like food.

Here are some sentences. Some of them are questions. Some of them are answers.

Put a question mark at the end of the questions. Put a full stop at the end of the answers.

What do you have for breakfast

I have toast

What do you drink at breakfast time

I have milk to drink

Can you write a question about food or drink?

_____

_____

Brodie's
Brain Booster

What is your favourite breakfast food?

Questions about birthdays

I get excited on my birthday.

When is your birthday?

My birthday is in June.

Copy out the question and the answer carefully. Remember to put capital letters in the right places.

_____

_____

Can you think of two more questions about birthdays?

_____

_____

_____

_____

Brodie's Brain Booster

What is your favourite birthday party game?

The sentences below are questions and answers.
Rewrite them correctly.

where are you going on holiday

_____

i am going to cornwall

_____

when are you going

_____

i think i am going in august

_____

who is going on holiday with you

_____

dad is coming with me

_____

Imogen's address

Imogen had lots of cards for her birthday.

Here is one of the envelopes.
It shows her address.

I don't know my postcode.

Miss Imogen Roberts
20 Bradford Road
Wellington
Sussex
BN31 2JE

Copy out the address very carefully. Make sure your capital letters match the ones on the envelope.

_____

_____

_____

_____

_____

Brodie's Brain Booster

Look carefully at an envelope showing your own address.

Imogen's address again

This envelope is missing its stamp!

Look carefully at Imogen's address.

This is her house number.

This is the town where she lives.

Miss Imogen Roberts
20 Bradford Road
Wellington
Sussex
BN31 2JE

This is Imogen's full name.

This is her road.

This is the county.

This is the postcode of Imogen's address. It is a mixture of capital letters and numbers.

Answer the questions below.

What is Imogen's surname?

_____

In what town does Imogen live?

_____

What is her postcode?

_____

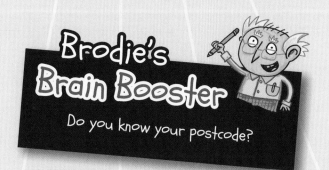

Brodie's
Brain Booster

Do you know your postcode?

33

Commas in addresses

Here is a letter to Imogen's grandparents.

Look at the special way of writing and**.**

Mr & Mrs Roberts,
57 Langley Road,
Holbury,
Dorset,
DT12 7QZ

The top line shows Mr **and** Mrs**.**

There is a comma at the end of each line.

Copy out the address very carefully. Make sure your capital letters and commas match the ones on the envelope.

_____

_____

_____

_____

_____

Brodie's Brain Booster

Have you ever visited relatives? Can you remember where they live?

Your address

You may need help with your address.

Let's build your address. Answer the questions to help you to get started.

What is your full name?

_____

Does your house have a number? If it does, what is the number?

_____

Does your house have a name? If it does, what is the name?

_____

What is the name of your road?

_____

Do you live in a town or a village or a city?

_____

What county do you live in?

_____

What is your postcode?

_____

Now put all the bits together to write your address.

_____

_____

_____

_____

Brodie's Brain Booster

You could write a letter to post to your relatives.

Colour in these exclamations in your favourite colours.

Wow!
Splat!
Boing!
Zoom!
Pow!

Brodie's Brain Booster

Look in your reading book. Can you find any exclamation marks?

Exclamation sentences

What a beautiful day!

Some sentences end with exclamation marks.

The exclamation sentence ends with an exclamation mark instead of a full stop.

Start here ➝ │

Finish with a dot. ⬅ •

Practise writing exclamation marks.

Now try smaller exclamation marks.

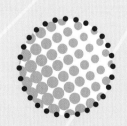

Brodie's Brain Booster

Look in your reading book. Can you find any exclamation sentences?

Can you remember how to write your address? Write it below.

_____

_____

_____

_____

_____

_____

The sentences below are all exclamations. Write them out correctly. Don't forget to end each one with an exclamation mark.

what a lovely view

_____

how sunny it is today

_____

what beautiful writing

_____

Practice pages

The names below have been written without capital letters at the start. Write them out correctly and put them into alphabetical order.

A B C D E F G H I J K L M N O P Q R S T U V W X Y Z

evan victor sasha yvonne xanthe oliver tegan una patek queenie

kate nick george zoe jez amy halina deepak isobel ricky

billy will lara faith cora megan

1 _____

2 _____

3 _____

4 _____

5 _____

6 _____

7 _____

8 _____

9 _____

10 _____

11 _____

12 _____

13 _____

14 _____

15 _____

16 _____

17 _____

18 _____

19 _____

20 _____

21 _____

22 _____

23 _____

24 _____

25 _____

26 _____

Practice pages

The place names below have been written without capital letters at the start. Write them out correctly.

india _____   france _____

spain _____   germany _____

poland _____   europe _____

belgium _____   australia _____

thailand _____   egypt _____

Can you think of five other place names?

_____

_____

_____

_____

_____

Write a sentence about a place you have visited.

_____

_____

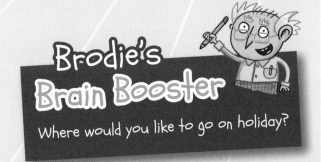

Brodie's
Brain Booster

Where would you like to go on holiday?

Practice pages

Every day of the week starts with a capital letter.

The days below have been written without capital letters at the start. Write them out correctly. Write them in the correct order. Start with Sunday.

wednesday   sunday   friday   tuesday   saturday   monday   thursday

---   ---

---   ---

---   ---

Which days are at the weekend?

Write a sentence about something that you do on the same day each week.

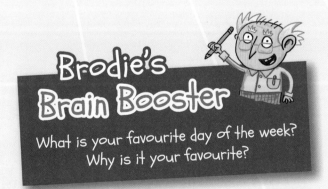

Brodie's Brain Booster

What is your favourite day of the week? Why is it your favourite?

41

Practice pages

Every month starts with a capital letter.

The months below have been written without capital letters at the start. Write them out correctly in the correct order. Start with January.

march   october   january   june   december   july

september   february   april   may   november   august

_____   _____

_____   _____

_____   _____

_____   _____

_____   _____

Write a sentence about one of the months.

_____

_____

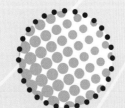

Brodie's Brain Booster

What is your favourite month? Why is it your favourite?

Practice pages

Every question sentence ends with a question mark.

The sentences below have not been written correctly. Some of them need question marks. Some need full stops. Write them correctly.

what time is it

_____

it is three o'clock

_____

shall we go out

_____

that is a good idea

_____

where would you like to go

_____

the park would be nice

_____

Brodie's
Brain Booster

Can you make up some questions?

Do you know when to use capital letters and full stops?

The sentences below are not written correctly. Write them correctly. There should be six sentences.

yesterday we went to the beach we took buckets and spades with us we played on the sand we made a sandcastle a big wave came and washed it away we moved up the beach and made a new one

_____

_____

_____

_____

_____

Brodie's
Brain Booster

Write about a special day that you have enjoyed.

The sentences below are not written correctly. Write them correctly.

we went on holiday on sunday on monday we went swimming on tuesday we played in the park we went to the beach on wednesday on thursday we had a ride on a train on friday we came home again

ANSWERS

Use the answers to check your child's progress but also to give prompts and ideas if they are needed. Note that sometimes your child's answer may not match the answer given here but could be just as good!

 p4

Check that your child has written the alphabet correctly in lower case and capital letters, and that her/his name is written correctly.

Brain Booster:

Help your child with the family names.

 p5

Alex	Noah
Borak	Ola
Celina	Pierre
Danek	Qadir
Eli	Robert
Faye	Sam
George	Tara
Hannah	Umi
Imogen	Vida
Jake	William
Kim	Xander
Lara	Yannik
Mia	Zara

Brain Booster:

Help your child think of appropriate names.

 p6

Sunday	Thursday
Monday	Friday
Tuesday	Saturday
Wednesday	

Saturday Sunday

Help your child to choose their favourite day.

Monday Tuesday Wednesday Thursday Friday

Brain Booster:

14

 p7

January	July
February	August
March	September
April	October
May	November
June	December

Help your child with the current month, the next month and the month of her/his birthday.

Brain Booster:

Your child could look at a calendar to find the numbers of days in the current month.

 p8

Brain Booster:

Talk to your child about countries that she/he has visited.

 p9

Check that your child has written the titles, authors and illustrators correctly.

Brain Booster:

Discuss your child's favourite book.

Progress Test 1

a b c d e f g h i j k l m n o p q r s t u v w x y z

A B C D E F G H I J K L M N O P Q R S T U V W X Y Z

Abbi	Maleeha
Joseph	Imogen

Help your child with the days, months and places.

 p11

Check your child's sentences.

Brain Booster:

Discuss your child's age and birthday.

p12

Check your child's sentences.

Brain Booster:

Discuss your child's favourite activity.

p13

Brain Booster:

Discuss family birthdays.

p14

Check your child's sentences.

Brain Booster:

Discuss the months.

p15

Check your child's sentences.

Brain Booster:

Look in your child's reading book for capital letters.

p16

Check your child's sentences.

Brain Booster:

Talk about countries with your child.

Progress Test 2

Check your child's sentences.

p18

Check your child's sentences.

Brain Booster:

Talk about London or other major cities.

p19

Check your child's sentences.

Brain Booster:

Discuss what happens on a regular Friday.

p20

Talk about weekend activities and help your child to compose sentences.

Brain Booster:

Talk about a bike ride or another activity your child enjoys.

p21

Check that your child has copied the rhyme accurately.

Brain Booster:

Look at rhymes with your child and discuss their format.

p22

Has your child copied the rhyme accurately?

Brain Booster:

Help your child to recite a poem.

p23

Check the thank you note.

Brain Booster:

Discuss presents your child has received in the past.

Progress Test 3

Check that your child has written the months correctly.

p25

Has your child written the question marks correctly?

Brain Booster:

Look for questions with your child.

p26

Has your child copied the sentences correctly?

Brain Booster:

Help your child to compose some questions.

p27

Check your child's questions.

Brain Booster:

Help your child to compose some more questions.

p28

Check that your child has written the answers appropriately.

Brain Booster:

Talk about questions that your child finds difficult.

p29

What do you have for breakfast?

I have toast.

What do you drink at breakfast time?

I have milk to drink.

Check your child's question.

Brain Booster:

Discuss favourite breakfast foods.

p30

Check that your child has written the answers appropriately.

Brain Booster:

Discuss your child's favourite party games.

Progress Test 4

Where are you going on holiday?

I am going to Cornwall.

When are you going?

I think I am going in August.

Who is going on holiday with you?

Dad is coming with me.

p32

Check that the address has been copied accurately.

Brain Booster:

Look at an addressed envelope with your child.

p33

Roberts
Wellington
BN31 2JE

Brain Booster:

Discuss your postcode with your child.

p34

Check that the address has been copied accurately.

Brain Booster:

Discuss the address of your child's relatives.

p35

Help your child to write your address.

Brain Booster:

If appropriate, help your child to write a letter to their relatives.

p36

Look at the use of exclamation marks with your child.

Brain Booster:

Help your child to find exclamation marks in the reading book.

p37

Has your child written the exclamation marks correctly?

Brain Booster:

Help your child to find exclamation sentences in the reading book.

Check that your child has written the address correctly.

What a lovely view!

How sunny it is today!

What beautiful writing!

 p39

Amy	Nick
Billy	Oliver
Cora	Patek
Deepak	Queenie
Evan	Ricky
Faith	Sasha
George	Tegan
Halina	Una
Isobel	Victor
Jez	Will
Kate	Xanthe
Lara	Yvonne
Megan	Zoe

 p40

India	France
Spain	Germany
Poland	Europe
Belgium	Australia
Thailand	Egypt

Help your child to think of place names and to write about a place they have visited.

Brain Booster:

Discuss ideas for holidays.

 p41

Sunday	Thursday
Monday	Friday
Tuesday	Saturday
Wednesday	

Saturday Sunday

Check your child's sentence.

Brain Booster:

Talk about a favourite day and why it is a favourite.

 p42

January	July
February	August
March	September
April	October
May	November
June	December

Check your child's sentence.

Brain Booster:

Talk about a favourite month and why it is a favourite.

 p43

What time is it?

It is three o'clock.

Shall we go out?

That is a good idea.

Where would you like to go?

The park would be nice.

Brain Booster:

Help your child to compose some questions.

p44

Yesterday we went to the beach. We took buckets and spades with us. We played on the sand. We made a sandcastle. A big wave came and washed it away. We moved up the beach and made a new one.

Brain Booster:

Check your child's writing about a special day.

Progress Test 6

We went on holiday on Sunday. On Monday we went swimming. On Tuesday we played in the park. We went to the beach on Wednesday. On Thursday we had a ride on a train. On Friday we came home again.